FAR OUT
CLASSIC STORIES
D0434271

INTRODUCING...

MR PRINCE
JOHNNY
SCARLET
TUCK
MARIAN
in...

Raintree is an imprint of Capstone Global Library Limited, a company incorporated in England and Wales having its registered office at 264 Banbury Road, Oxford, OX2 7DY – Registered company number: 6695582

www.raintree.co.uk
myorders@raintree.co.uk

Edited by Abby Huff
Designed by Hilary Wacholz
Original illustrations © Capstone Global Library Limited 2020
Originated by Capstone Global Library Ltd
Printed and bound in India

978 1 4747 9447 3

British Library Cataloguing in Publication Data
A full catalogue record for this book is available from the British Library.

ROBIN HOOD, TIME TRAVELLER

A GRAPHIC NOVEL

WRITTEN BY BENJAMIN HARPER
ILLUSTRATED BY ALEX LOPEZ

Year: 2167
SPACE BURGER
At just twelve years old, Robin Hood was already a tech genius. He invented time travel devices for a company called Time Minders.
Rubbish traffic!

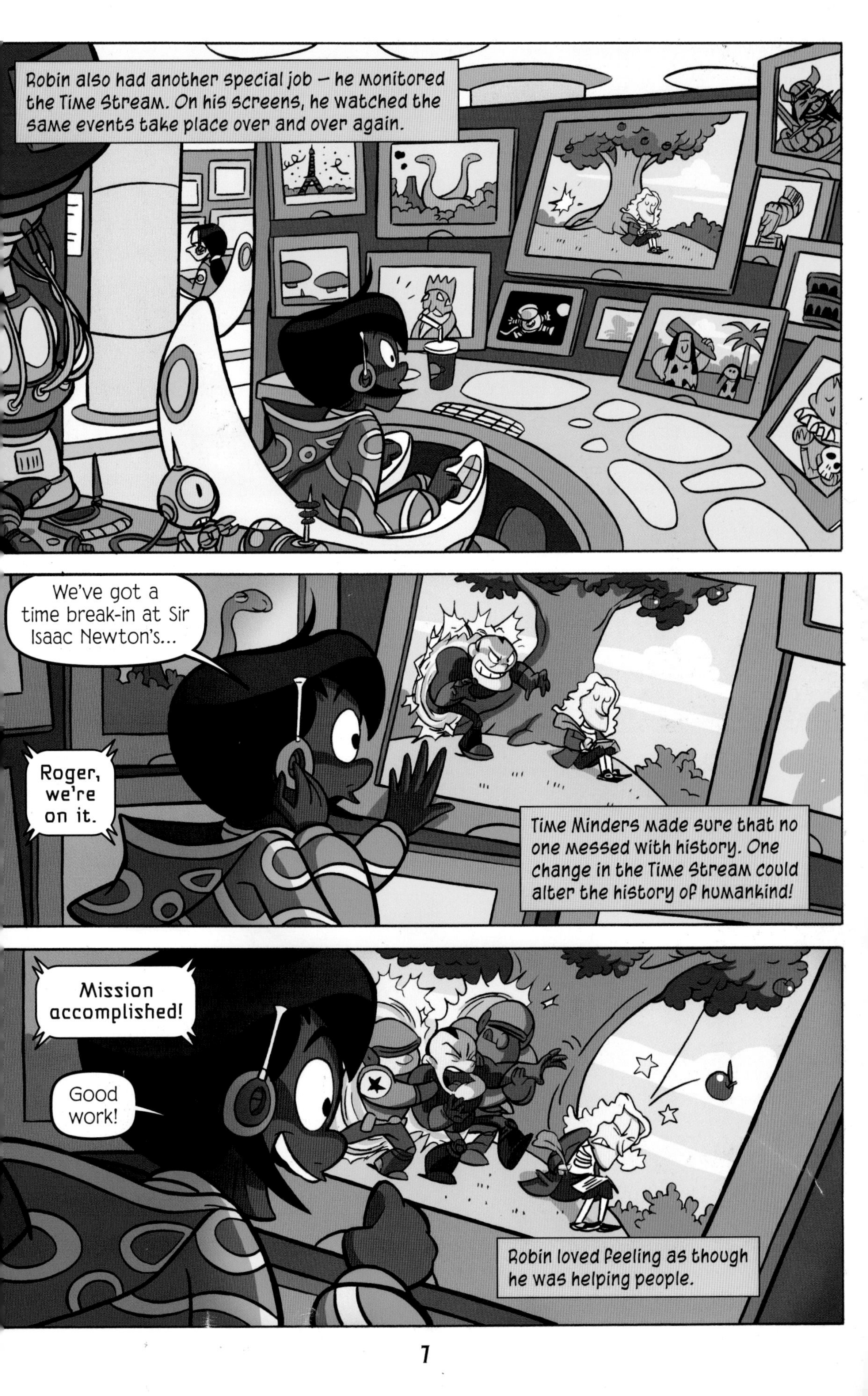
Robin also had another special job — he monitored the Time Stream. On his screens, he watched the same events take place over and over again.
We've got a time break-in at Sir Isaac Newton's...
Roger, we're on it.
Time Minders made sure that no one messed with history. One change in the Time Stream could alter the history of humankind!
Mission accomplished!
Good work!
Robin loved feeling as though he was helping people.

And Robin loved making new gadgets.
Ladies and gentlemen, I give you the future of time travel – the *PortaPortal!*
With this handheld device, I can travel anywhere, any time. Just watch!
WOOOSH!!!
Ung?
Ooooohhh!
CLAP!
CLAP!
CLAP!

Mr Prince was the CEO of Time Minders. He loved Robin's inventions – and the money that they made the company.
CLAP! CLAP!
I think I told you that Robin was a genius?
The future is here!
But back at his desk, Robin continued to watch the same events over and over again – and the same problems.
He didn't like seeing *anyone* in trouble.
I wish we could help people in the past.
If we did that, we could accidentally change history. Plus, it's against company policy!

The more Robin watched, the more he wished he could *do* something.
It's all just so unfair!
Sob!
I'll take that, if you don't mind.
My lunch!
Oh no! This is my favourite dress.
What a shame.

But this is the only food we have!
And I'm taking it as your tax. Be thankful I'm not taking anything else.
TAXES
THAT'S ENOUGH!
I've got to do what's right. I'll travel through time and help when I know it won't interfere with history.
Making sure people's feelings aren't hurt or that they don't go hungry can't change the Time Stream...
To-Do List:
-Feed the hungry
-Protect the poor
-Get that kid's sandwich back

Can it?

Robin grabbed his bag of inventions and powered up his PortaPortal.
Here we go!
Wait! That is company property! You're breaking the ru–
SWOOSH...
66 million BC
MAY 7 1981
1651
1492
FEBRUARY
MARCH
1951 NOVEM
1883
AAAAAAAAAAAAAAHHH!!!
JULY
237

WOOOOOOOOSH!!!
THUD!
Robin had arrived. He was starting his quest in ...
The Cretaceous Period.
Time for my first good deed!

There's the little dino now.
ROOOOOOAR!!
Gulp!
Robin took out one of his favourite gadgets.
Take this, bully!
SHOOOP!

Robin had saved the day!
Now you can finally have your supper.
Well, onto the next good deed. Huh?
SOB!
What's the matter? Are you all alone?
Mm-hmm.
I know! You can help me help others.
Raar!
With my handy Universal Translator, I'll even understand what you're saying.
You'll need a human name, though. How about Scarlet?
I love it!
Great! Let's go, Scarlet!

Meanwhile, back at Time Minders...
That annoying do-gooder! I can't believe Robin is doing this.
He knows it's against code 4.23-X to interfere with past events!
Bad stuff happens and things are unfair. That's just life!
One wrong move, and the Time Stream could change forever. Life as we know it could go...
KABOOOOM!

I'll stop him. Even if I have to jump from century ...
... to century. I won't rest until I capture Robin Hood!

Next stop: the 15th century.
The villagers should be here somewhere.
What on earth are you wearing?
Look – a dragon!

We can't do anything if we stand out!
Here, put this on.
That's better. Now, onto helping people!

Robin soon got his chance.
Please, give it back!
Over here, Scarlet.
But Sheriff, that is all we have!
Our family will starve.
TAXES
Tell that to the prince. You haven't paid your taxes, and we are collecting.
We worked all year to grow these crops. It's just not fair!
Pshaw. The law is the law. Now out of our way! We've got more taxes to collect.

Oi, bully! Leave them alone!
PPPPPPPFFFFFFFT!
How darest thou speak to me like that!
Take this!
TAXES
I'll put you in irons! You churl*!
Just try to catch me!
*Medieval insult!
The Sheriff of Nottingham chased Robin into the dark woods.
Give yourself up, boy!
Never! Justice will always win!
TAXES
SHERWOOD FOREST
ENTER AT YOUR OWN RISK!
I'll show him. I'll just set my Animal Attract 2.0...
BEAR

The sheriff finally found Robin.
You've got an appointment with the stocks!
You should be in stocks. You're stealing from innocent people and giving to the rich.
Puh-lease. Spare me the lecture—
Huh?
SHF
SHHF
ROOOAR!!
EEEEKKK!
TAXES
You'll have a lot of time now to think about how you should treat people.
I shan't be left in this tree! I shan't!
TAXES

Wow! With all this, the villagers won't be hungry for quite a while!
Great! Let's go!
TAXES
Robin and Scarlet headed back to the village.
Gather round, everyone! I have something for you from that sheriff.
TAXES
Thank you!
You're very kind!

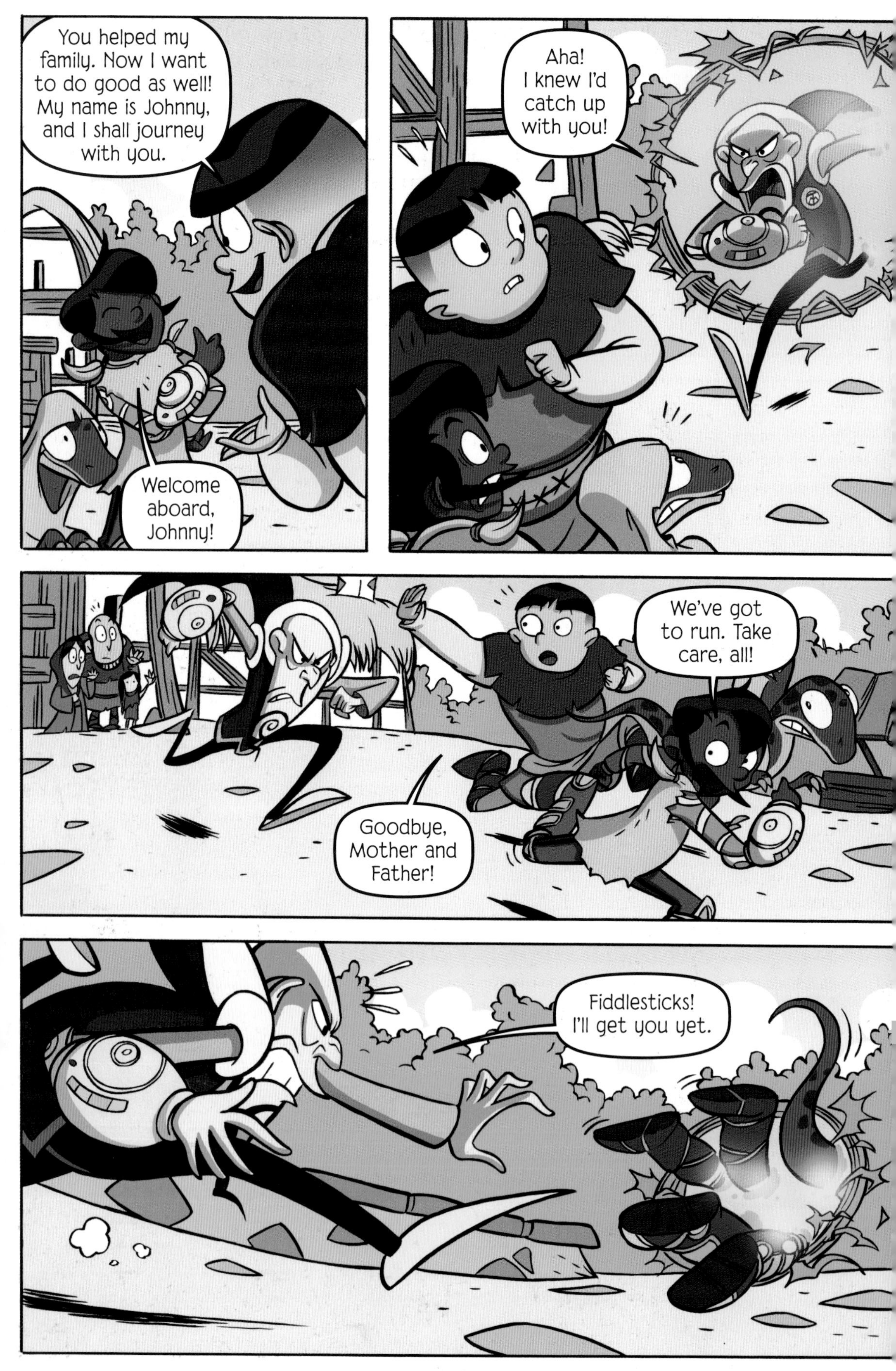

You helped my family. Now I want to do good as well! My name is Johnny, and I shall journey with you.
Welcome aboard, Johnny!
Aha! I knew I'd catch up with you!
We've got to run. Take care, all!
Goodbye, Mother and Father!
Fiddlesticks! I'll get you yet.

Next stop: 1956
Be careful, Marian. That is your best dress, and we can't afford another one.
Yes, Mother.
What did I tell you about walking on my pavement?
Please, leave me alone!
Robin had watched the bully push Marian into the mud many times before. Now he was putting a stop to it!
SWOOOSH!
Incoming!
!

A MONSTER!
HEEEEEEELP!
That was easier than I expected!
Totally!
Who are you three? What's with the giant lizard?
That's Scarlet, the dinosaur! I'm Robin, and this is Johnny. We travel through time to help people.
Hello.
Ooh that sounds fun! I'm Marian.
Hey!
If you want to come, Marian, now is your chance. LET'S GO!

You think you've got away, Robin. But I'll be ready for you.
The year: 2020, at an ordinary school...
Now we need to make sure that bully doesn't take that boy's lunch!
Wait a minute–
TECH CONTEST!
Best gadget wins £100,000.
See Mr McCully in Room 4 for details.
A tech contest?! I'm brilliant at inventing! If I enter and win, we could give the prize money to people in need.
Are you *sure* you can win?
It's in the bag.

4D
Let's get the competition details...
I've got him this time!
Wait, that voice sounds familiar. It's...
Mr Prince!
I know Robin will enter this tech contest. When he does, I'll nab him *and* his PortaPortal!
Ha ha ha ha ha!
Mr Prince is setting a trap! But I'll still enter the competition. And I'll win.
Be careful, Robin!

Later, Robin and his friends worked and worked on a new gadget.
With all these parts, I am sure we'll come up with the best invention.
There! It's finished.
It's beautiful!
I cannot wait to see what it does.
What do you call it?
It's the BULLY AWAY BETA!
And I think it may come in handy in more way than one.

At the competition...
Tech Contest Judging Today!
There are so many other pupils here.
Don't worry. We can win this!
I'll just put on my disguise...
Next...
This is Robin. I can spot him anywhere!
And what do you have, young man?
This is a device I've made.

GOTCHA, Robin Hood! I knew you couldn't resist this competition! Your days of jumping through time and helping people are *over*!
And now, ladies and gentlemen, I present ... the Bully Away Beta in action!
CLICK!
ZWOOOOOONG!!
Huh?
You see, my device spots and temporarily freezes bullies. That gives would-be victims time to escape.
Genius! My dear boy, you are the winner! Here is your prize.
Robin had saved the day! And this time, Mr Prince wouldn't be able to follow him.

But before Robin and his friends left, there was one more task to take care of.
This bully won't take your lunch ever again!
Thanks. He's been stealing my sandwiches for the whole term.
You're welcome. We love to help people.
I'm Tuck. Who are you lot?
I'm Marian. That's Robin, Johnny and Scarlet.
We time travel to help out those in need!

Can I come too? I'd love to help.
The more, the *merrier*!
On to the next adventure!

ALL ABOUT THE ORIGINAL STORY!

Robin Hood is the subject of ballads and poems dating back to the 15th century. We don't know who wrote most of these early tales. In 1883, American author Howard Pyle published *The Merry Adventures of Robin Hood*. The novel gathered many of the Robin Hood legends into one book and helped make the character popular.

Robin's story varies from tale to tale, but in most of them he is a nobleman who is loyal to King Richard, the ruler of England. The king is away fighting in a religious war, and his brother Prince John has taken control of the land. The prince is cruel and greedy. He sends the Sheriff of Nottingham to collect unfair taxes from his subjects. Robin is against this. So he robs from the sheriff and gives the money back to the poor.

Robin doesn't work alone. He has help from a group of outlaws called the Merry Men. The Merry Men include Little John, Will Scarlet and Friar Tuck. Robin also falls in love with a noblewoman called Maid Marian. She joins the fight to help the common people.

In one adventure, the Sheriff of Nottingham comes up with a plan to capture Robin. He organizes an archery competition with a prize of a solid gold arrow. Robin is famous for his skill with a bow, and the sheriff knows Robin will enter the competition. Sure enough, Robin decides to compete, even though the Merry Men warn him that it's a trap. But Robin puts on a disguise, and the sheriff doesn't recognize him. Robin easily wins and collects his prize. Later, Robin and his men shoot an arrow with a letter tied to it into the sheriff's home. The letter tells the sheriff that *he* is the one who's been tricked. He gave the golden arrow to his greatest enemy – Robin Hood!

A FAR OUT GUIDE TO THE STORY'S FUTURISTIC TWISTS

The original Robin Hood was a skilled archer from the past. In this version, he's a tech genius from the future!

The Merry Men were people from all over England. Here, Robin's group is made up of children throughout time!

The unfair ruler Prince John has been replaced by Mr Prince, the uncaring CEO of Time Minders.

In both tales, Robin outsmarts a trap set up to capture him. But instead of an archery competition, he wins a technology competition!

VISUAL QUESTIONS

The way characters are drawn can give you hints about their personalities. Look at this panel. What in the art and text tells you that Mr Prince might not be a very kind person?

That annoying do-gooder! I can't believe Robin is doing this.
1

Why is the text coming out of the word balloon? How does it connect to the action happening in the panel?

What is making the "SHF SHHF" noise behind the sheriff on page 22? Were you surprised by it? Why or why not?

e artist decided not to use traditional panels on page 10. What feeling
oes it create to see all the computer screens at once? How is this momen
portant to Robin's decision to leave Time Minders?

this story, Robin Hood is a tech
enius. Look through the book
nd find three examples of when
s gadgets help solve a problem.

AUTHOR

Benjamin Harper has worked as an editor at Lucasfilm LTD. and DC Comics. He currently lives in Los Angeles, USA, where he writes, watches monster films and plays with his cat, Edith Bouvier Beale III. His other books include the *Bug Girl* series, *Obsessed with Star Wars*, *Rolling with BB-8* and *Hansel & Gretel & Zombies.*

ILLUSTRATOR

Alex Lopez is from Sabadell, Spain. He became a professional illustrator and comic book artist in 2001, but he has been drawing ever since he can remember. Lopez's pieces have been published in many countries, including the United States, United Kingdom, Spain, France, Italy, Belgium and Turkey. He's also worked on a variety of projects, from illustrated books to computer games to marketing pieces ... but what he loves most is making comic books.

GLOSSARY

alter change something, but not completely

capture catch and hold something by using force

Cretaceous Period period of time that lasted from about 145 to 65 million years ago, when many types of dinosaurs lived on Earth

device machine made to do a specific job

gadget small electronic tool or machine

invention new idea or machine, usually made after studying a problem and working to find the best way to solve it

medieval period of history between 500 and 1450

monitor watch or check on something closely over a period of time

quest long and often difficult journey made to achieve a special goal

stocks wooden frame with holes to hold a person's feet or hands that was once used as a way to punish people

translator something (such as a special high-tech invention) that can change words from one language into another language

victim person who is harmed, cheated or fooled by someone else

NEW SPINS

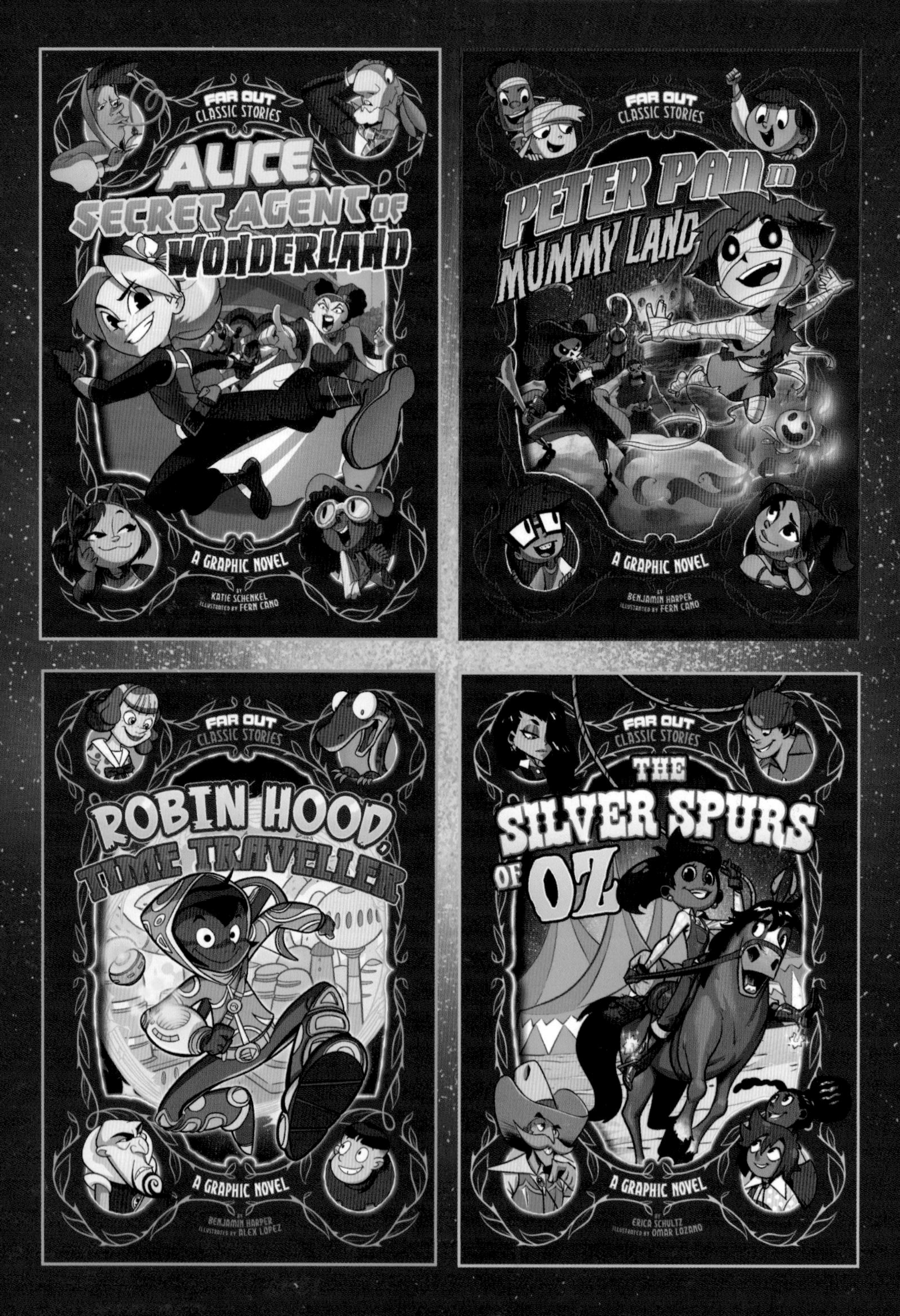

FAR OUT CLASSIC STORIES